S. Wilkinson   R. Nakata   K. Frazier

Let's Speak English

Workbook 1

Oxford University Press
1993

Alphabet Practice

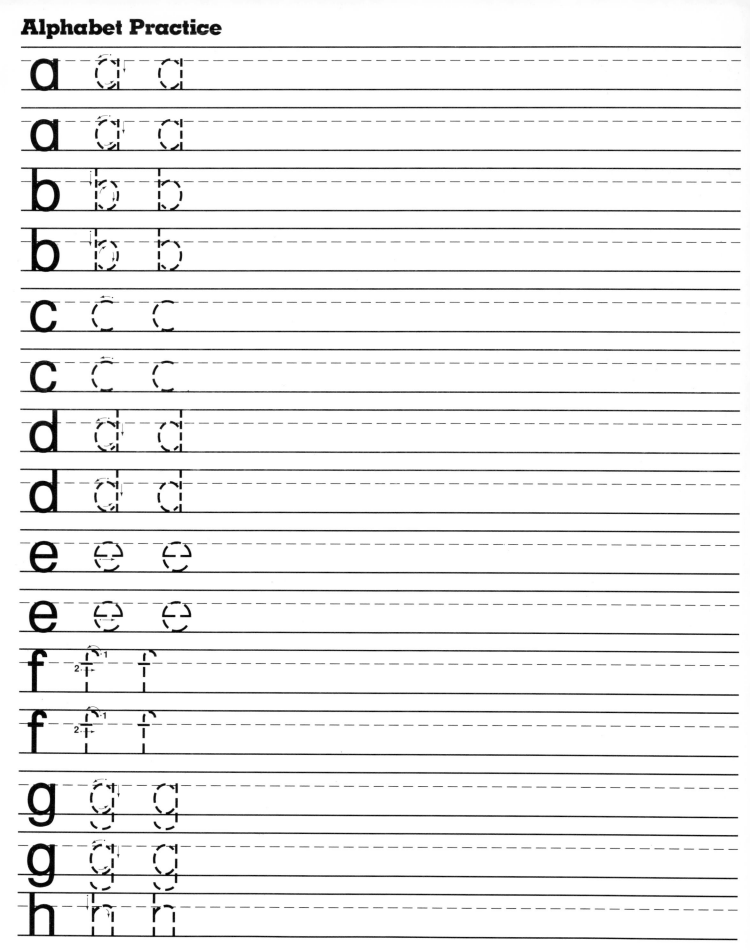

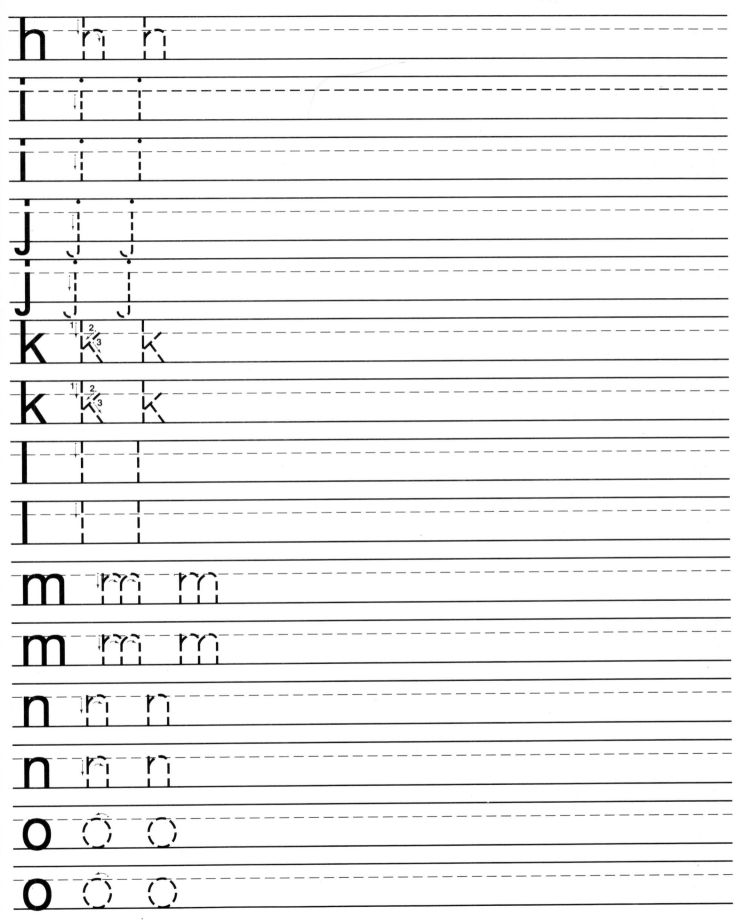

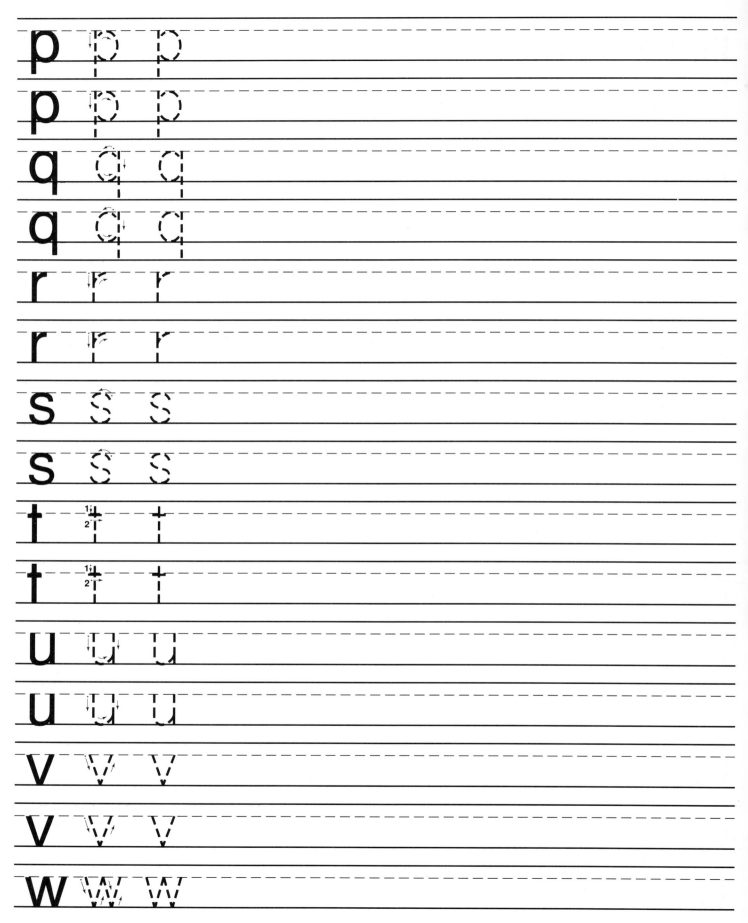

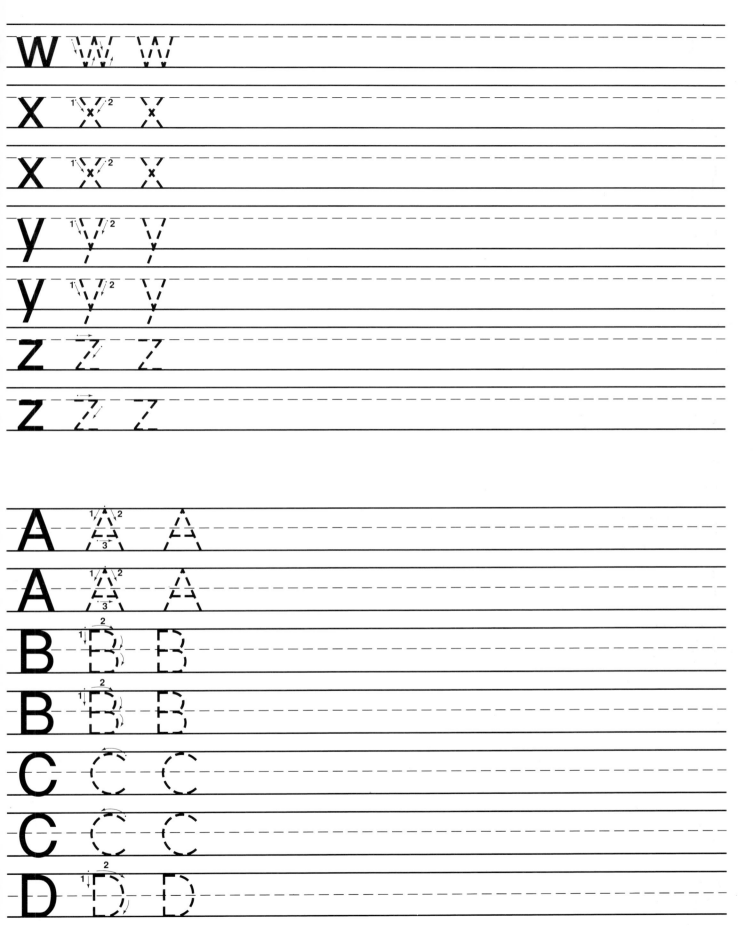

W

X

X

y

y

z

z

A

A

B

B

C

C

D

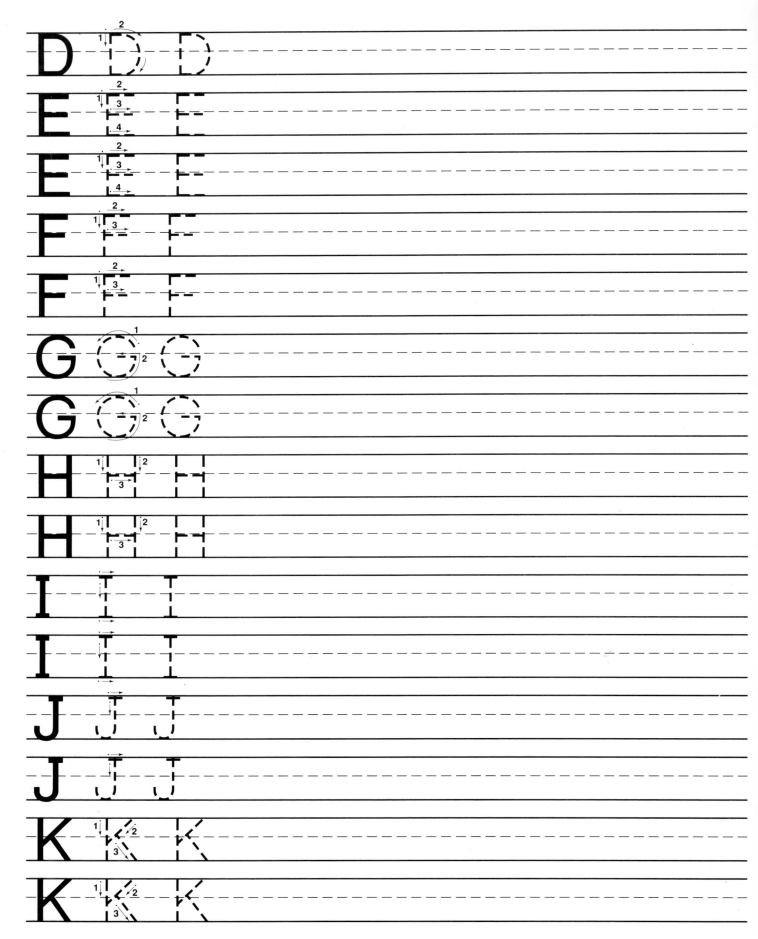

6

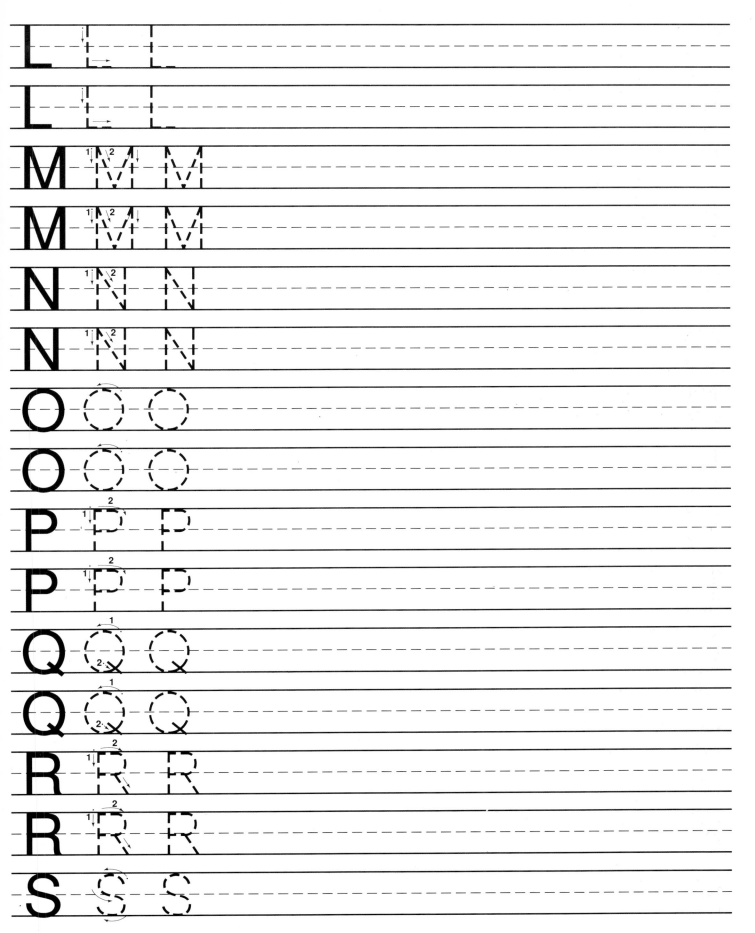

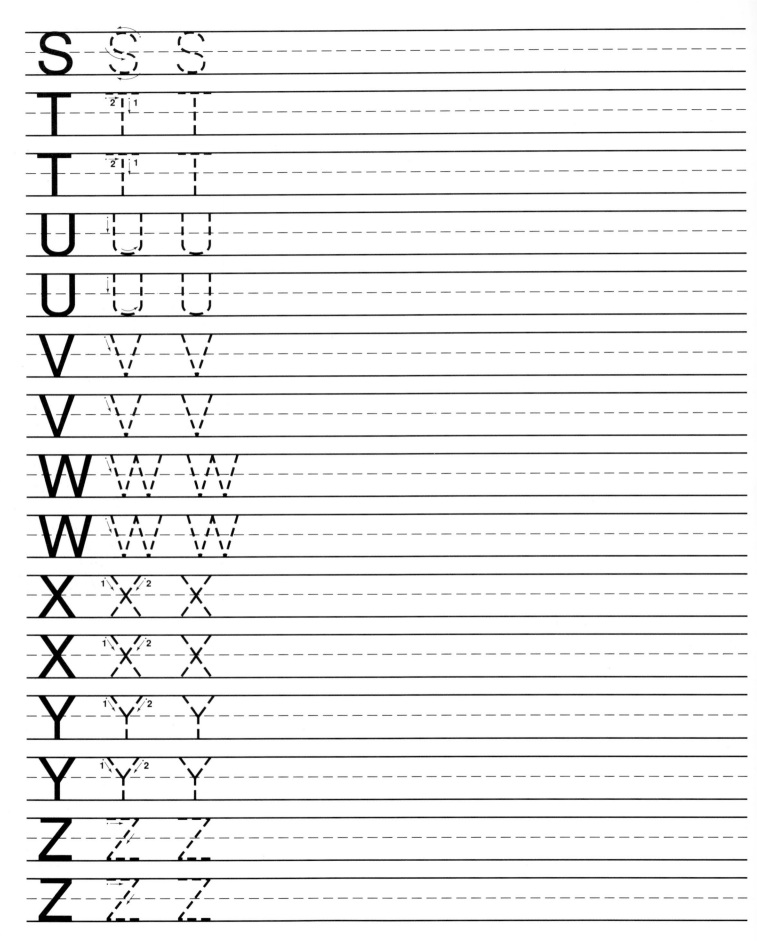

8

Unit 1

Trace and join.

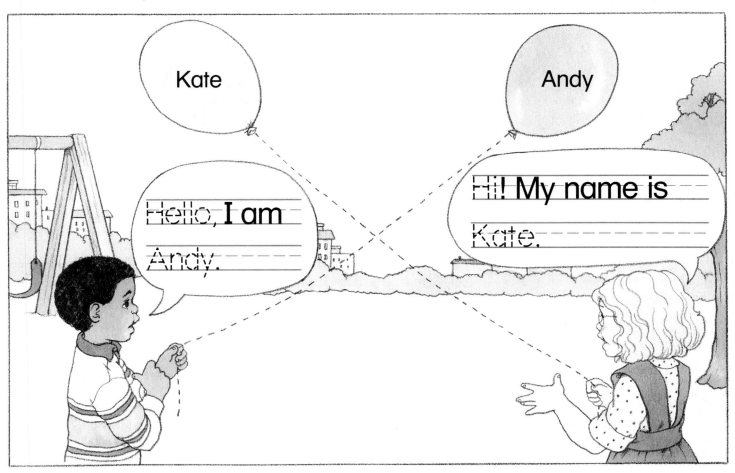

Kate

Andy

Hello, I am Andy.

Hi! My name is Kate.

Write your name.

What's your name?

My name is _____.

Trace.

What is this?

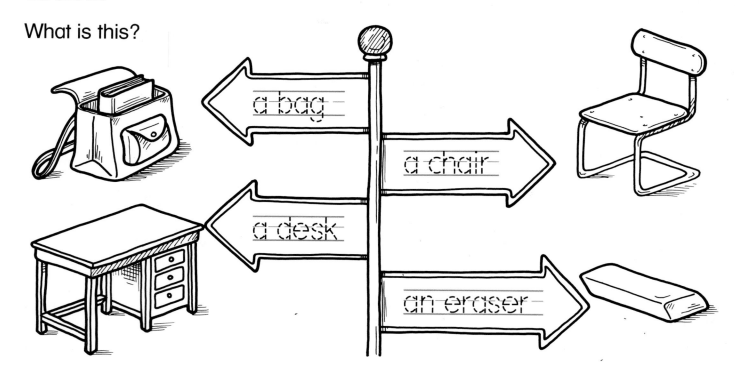

a bag

a chair

a desk

an eraser

Trace.

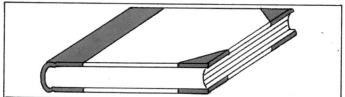

It is a pencil.

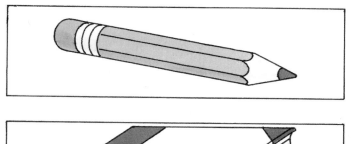

It is a book.

Draw and write.

It is _____.

10

Trace and join.

It's a book.

It's a desk.

It's a chair.

It's a bag.

It's a pencil.

It's a ruler.

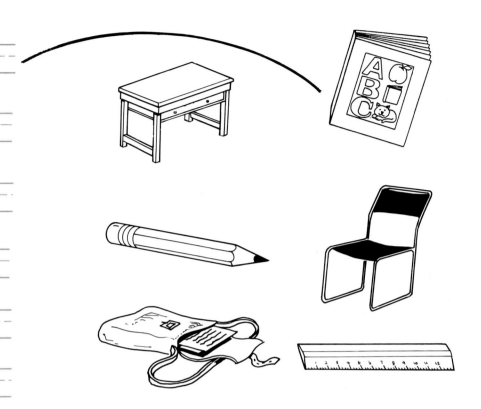

Join and trace.

It is

What is

What's

It's

Join.

What's your name?   It's a book.

What's this?   My name's Kate.

Circle the answer.

Is this a pencil?

(Yes, it is.)

No, it is not.

Is this a book?

Yes, it is.

No, it is not.

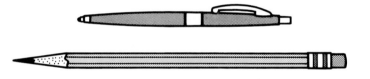

Is this a desk?

Yes, it is.

No, it is not.

Is this a ruler?
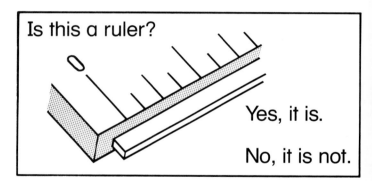
Yes, it is.

No, it is not.

Trace.

Is this a desk?

~~Yes,~~ it is.

Is this a chair?
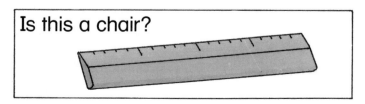
~~No,~~ it is not.

Trace and join.

is not

it is

what is

what's

isn't

it's

Write and trace.

name?

this?

pencil?

book?

My name's Jenny.

It's an eraser.

No, it isn't. It's a pen.

Yes, it is.

Write and trace.

Hello.   Jenny.

What's   ?

this?

an eraser?

a pencil?

Hi!   Lisa.

My name   Andy.

bag.

No,

Yes,

13

Trace. Join the letters.

A a b c d e f g h i j k l m n

B 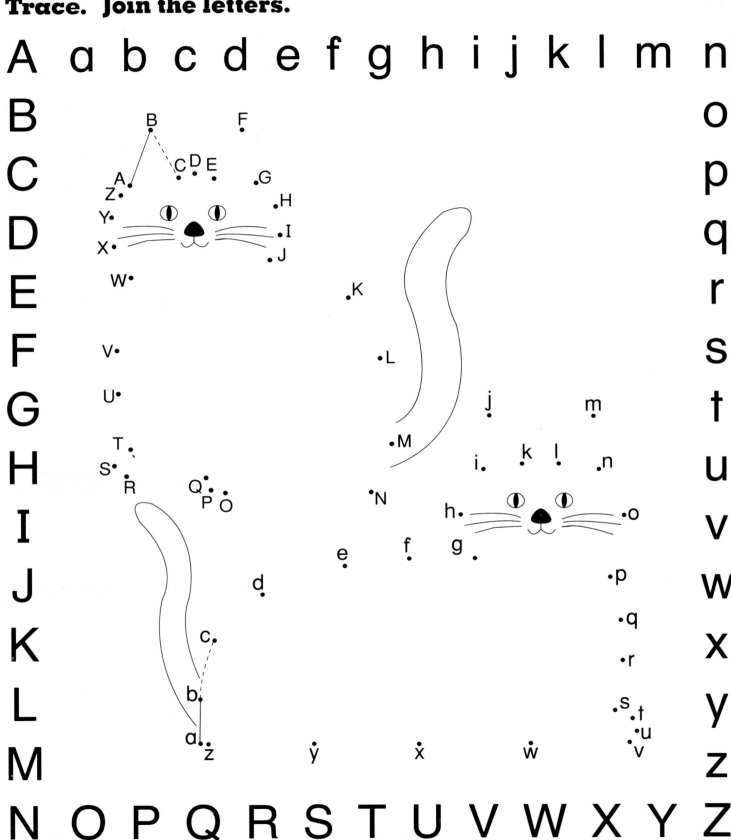 o

C p

D q

E r

F s

G t

H u

I v

J w

K x

L y

M z

N O P Q R S T U V W X Y Z

Trace and say.

Please be quiet.

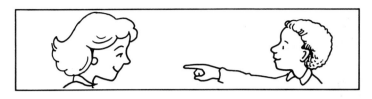

Point to the teacher.

Touch your desk.

Listen carefully.

Join and trace.

Open your book.

Close your book.

Stand up.

Sit down.

Circle and trace.

What is this?

a book

a bag

It is a book.

What is this?

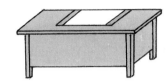

a chair

a desk

It is a desk.

Circle and write.

What is this?

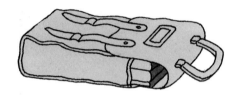

a bag

a pencil

It is _____ .

Trace.

Is this a ruler?

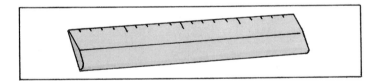

Yes, it is.

Is this a pen?

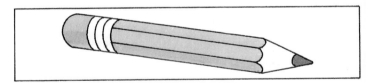

No, it is not.

Write.

Is this an eraser?

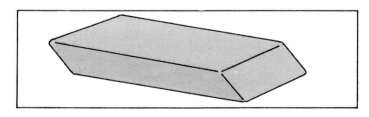

_____ , it is.

Unit 2

Trace.

Trace.

I am fine, thank you.

Trace, colour, and write.

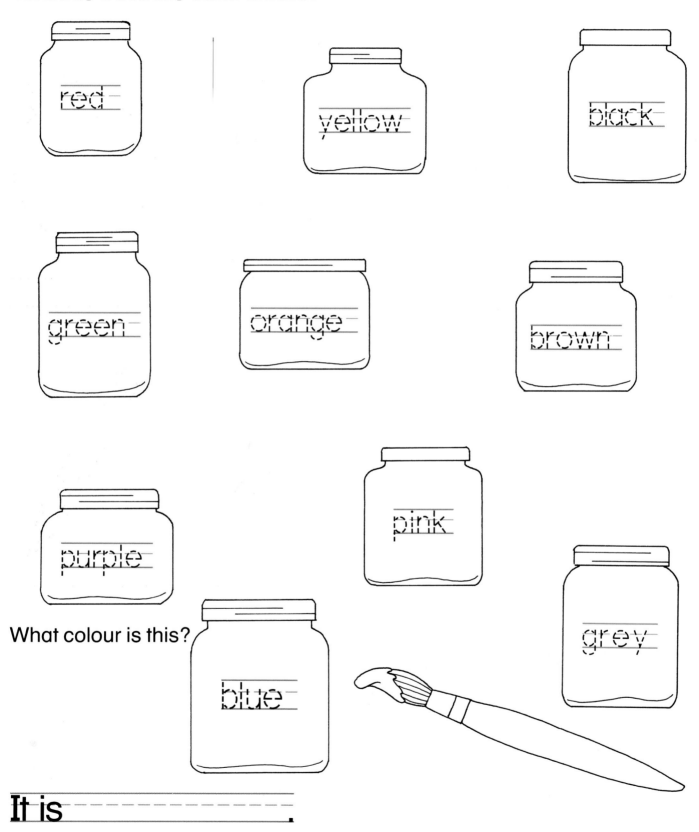

red

yellow

black

green

orange

brown

purple

pink

grey

What colour is this?

blue

It is _____.

18

Colour, trace, and write.

black

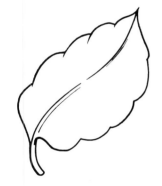

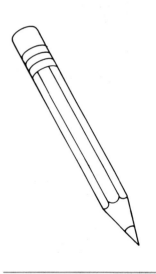

Trace and write colours.

p----ple

o----ge

y----ow

g----y

br----n

w----te

Colour, trace, and say.

pink

purple

brown

This is a pink pen.

This is a purple bag.

This is a brown book.

green

yellow

This is a green and yellow ruler.

20

Colour, trace, and write.

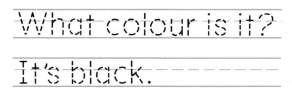

What colour is it?

It's black.

What

It's

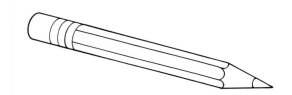

Say and colour.

This is an orange book.

This is a brown chair.

This is a grey eraser.

This is a blue and yellow bag.

This is a red and green apple.

This is a black cat.

Join and trace.

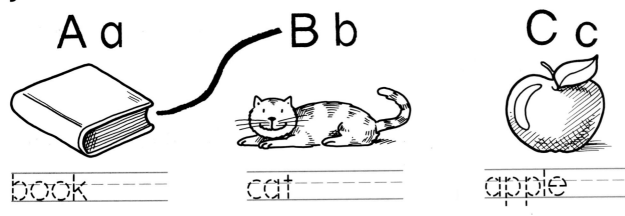

A a   B b   C c

book   cat   apple

Circle.

a b c   a b c   a b c

Trace.

a   apple   A   Andy

b   book   b   bag

c   cat   c   cloud

Join and say.

Take out your book.

Put your book away.

Put your hand up.

Put your hand down.

Write your name.

Pick up your pencil.

Put your pencil down.

Look at the board.

Colour, trace, and write.

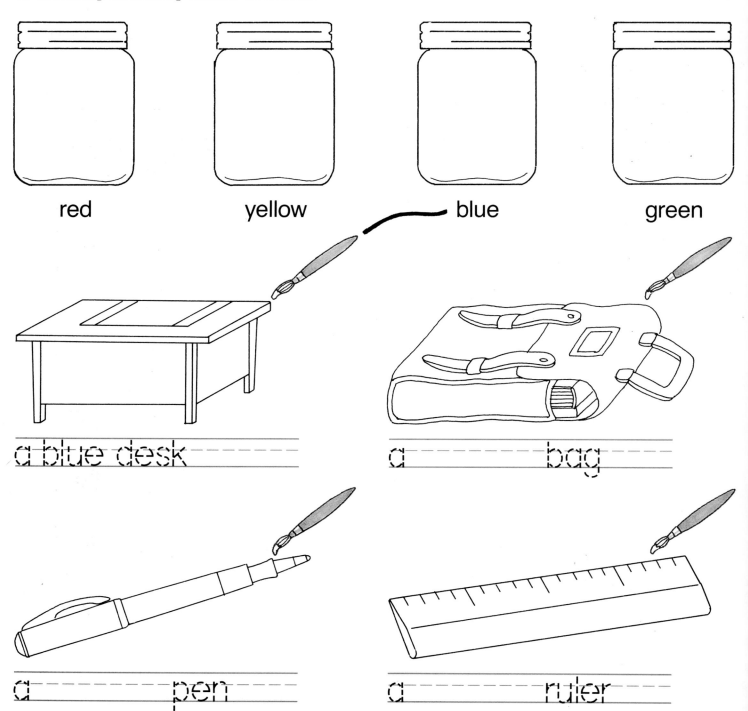

red   yellow   blue   green

a blue desk

a _____ bag

a _____ pen

a _____ ruler

Trace the alphabet.

a b c d e f g h i j k l m n o p q r s t u v w x y z

Review

1. Trace.

m	A	q	E	F	G	e	L	a	b
P	B	C	D	Q	H	k	y	D	c
r	S	o	W	f	I	M	p	e	d
T	u	M	L	K	J	c	J	f	R
P	O	N	g	Y	j	i	h	g	N
Q	w	n	I	I	k	G	i	Q	e
R	S	T	U	m	n	s	t	u	v
o	H	f	V	F	O	r	X	S	w
t	Y	X	W	I	p	q	J	y	x
B	Z	j	k	K	V	E	r	z	N

2. Write and join.

A a

B b

C c

_____ at

a pple

_____ ook

3. Circle and write.

What is this?

a book

a bag

It is _____ .

What is this?

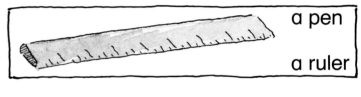

a pen

a ruler

It is _____ .

4. Write and colour.

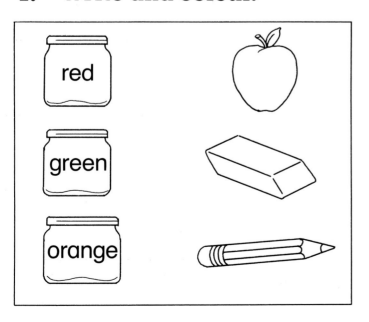

red

green

orange

a _____ apple

a _____ eraser

an _____ pencil

Unit 3

Join and trace.

Trace, write, and draw.

This is my friend, _____ .

Trace and write.

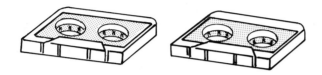

What's this?
It's a pencil case.

What are these?
They're cassettes.

Join.

It is	They're
They are	What's
What is	It's
I am	It isn't
It is not	I'm

28

Circle.

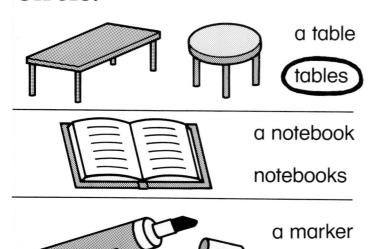

a table
(tables)

a pen

pens

a notebook

notebooks

a pencil case

pencil cases

a marker

markers

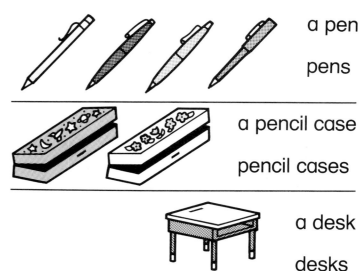

a desk

desks

Circle and trace.

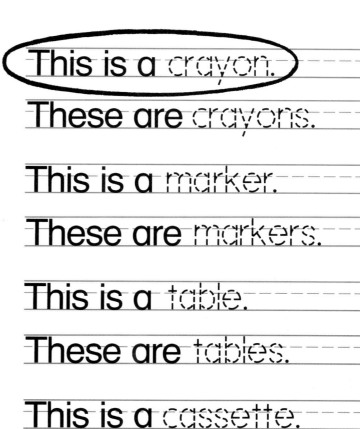

This is a crayon.

These are crayons.

This is a marker.

These are markers.

This is a table.

These are tables.

This is a cassette.

These are cassettes.

Trace, join, and write.

five

seven

ten

eight

two

three

nine

six

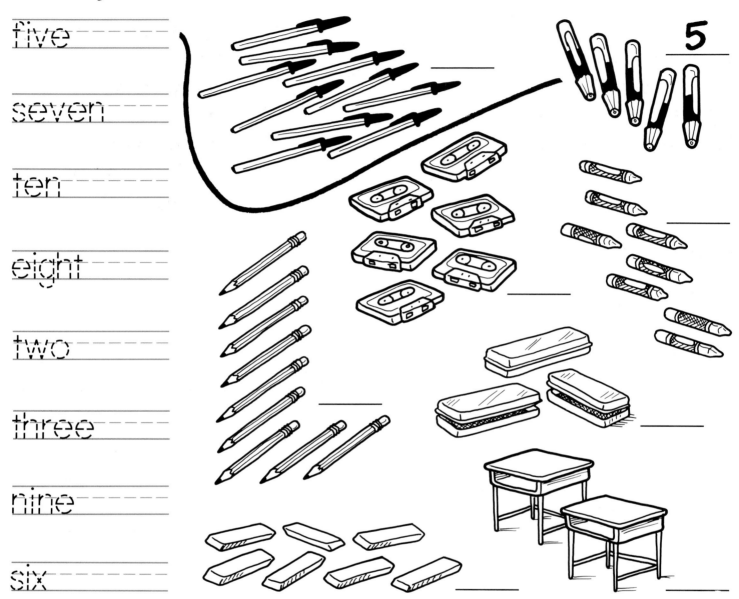

5

Trace.

one cat

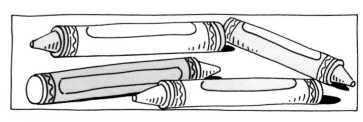

four crayons

Join.

This is my friend, John.
Is this a pen?
What's this?
What colour is it?
Hi, Jenny. How are you?
Hello, Lisa.
What are these?

No, it isn't. It's a pencil.
It's a bag.
It's blue and red.
Hi, John.
They're markers.
I'm fine, thank you.
Hello, Kate.

Trace and write.

How many?

two trainers

Join and trace.

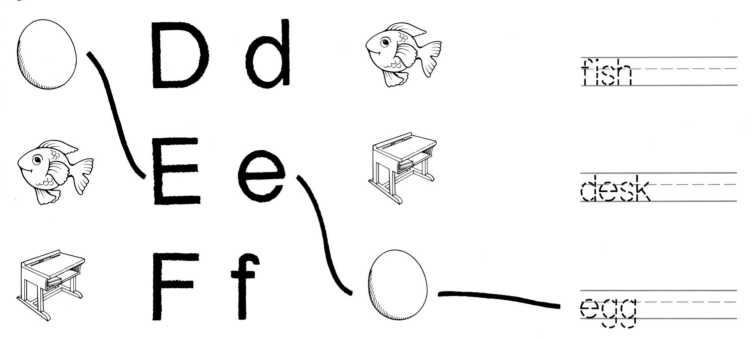

D d   fish

E e   desk

F f   egg

Trace.

d   desk   dog   door   d

e   egg   eraser   eight   e

f   fish   four   five   f

Join and say.

Go to the door.

Make a circle.

Make two lines.

Give me the crayon.

Draw a picture.

Come here.

Circle, write, and trace.

Count the boys.

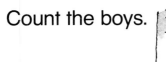

one

two

boys

Count the girls.

four

five

girls

Circle.

 this

these

 this

these

 this

these

Circle, write, and trace.

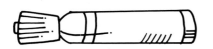 This

These

 This

These

is a marker.   are pens.

Circle, write, and trace.

How many?

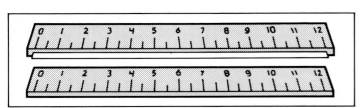

two

ten

rulers

four

five

erasers

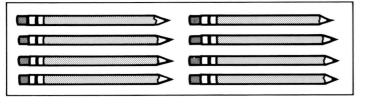

seven

eight

pencils

34

Unit 4

Trace.

It's nice to meet you.

It's nice to meet you, too.

Draw and trace.

This is my family.

Trace.

Who is he?

He is my father.

He is my brother.

Who is she?

She is my sister.

She is my grandmother.

Circle.

he

she

he

she

he

she

Trace and write the questions.

Who's he?

He's my father.

She's my mother.

She's my sister.

He's my brother.

Trace and write.

grandfather

g

f

m

John

b

s

Join.

Who's he? ——————— She's my sister.

Who's she? He's my friend.

What's this? They're crayons.

What are these? It's a fish.

Join and trace.

old

fat

ugly

pretty

young

thin

Circle, write, and trace.

tall

short

He is _____.

young

old

She is _____.

ugly

pretty

She is _____.

fat

thin

He is _____.

Trace and write.

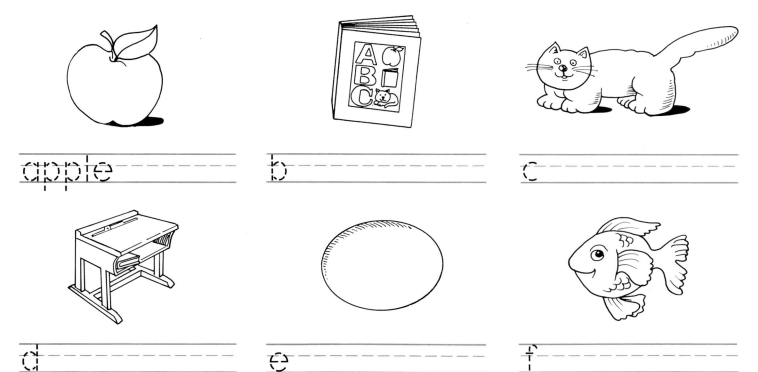

apple

b

c

d

e

f

Trace and write.

young   old   tall   short   pretty   ugly   thin   fat

He's tall.

She's

Trace.

girl

ink

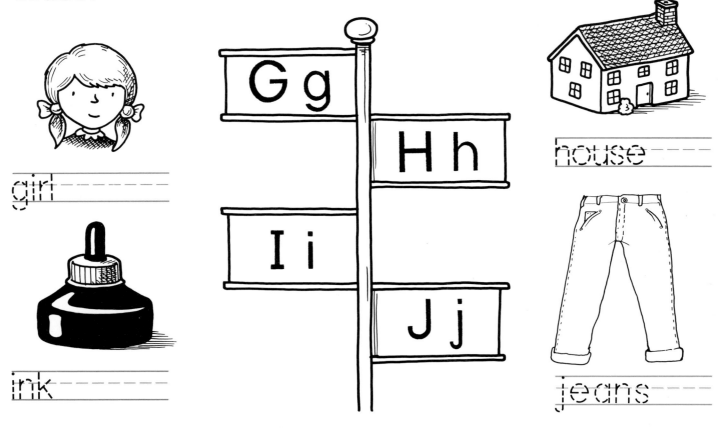

G g

H h

I i

J j

house

jeans

Circle and write.

g
(h)
i
j

h ouse

g
h
i
j

___ nk

G
H
I
J

___ enny

g
h
i
j

___ randfather

40

Join and trace.

go to sleep

wake up

eat your dinner

tidy up

play the piano

do your homework

Trace.

Don't watch TV.

Don't make a mess.

Circle and trace.

He is ugly.

He is pretty.

She is old.

She is young.

She is tall.

She is short.

Join and trace.

sister

grandfather

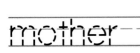

mother

brother

grandmother

father

42

Review

1. Write.

Across

3.

5.

7.

Down

1.

2.

4.

6.

2. Circle.

   he   she

   he   she

   he   she

   he   she

3. Trace and join.

one

eight

three

two

four

five

six

seven

1   2   3   4   5   6   7   8

4. Write.

old
young

tall
short

He is —————————— .

She is ————— .

She is —————————— .

He is —————————— .

44

Unit 5
Count and write.

I am **6** years old.

I am ___ years old.

I am ___ years old.

Trace, write, and draw.

How old are you?

I am ------- years old.

Trace.

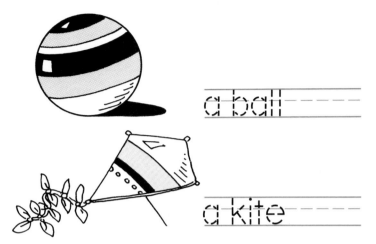

a ball

a kite

a car

a doll

Trace and write.

| What is it? | What is it? |

It is _____.

It is _____.

| What is it? | What is it? |

It is _____.

It is _____.

46

Trace and write questions and answers.

How old are you?
I'm seven.

How old _____ ?

_____ old _____ ?

_____ you?

Trace and write.

It's a kite.

It's a _____

47

Circle and trace.

Is it a yo-yo?

Yes, it is.

No, it is not.

Yes, it is.

Is it a skipping rope?

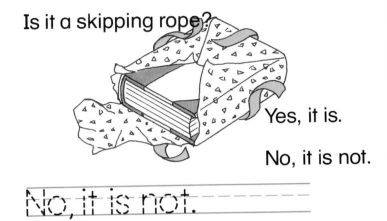

Yes, it is.

No, it is not.

No, it is not.

Circle and write.

Is it a bicycle?

Yes, it is.

No, it is not.

Is it a robot?

Yes, it is.

No, it is not.

Circle and trace.

big

little

big

little

a   cat

a   cat

48

Trace, write, and join.

It's a little kite.

_____ kite.

_____ round box.

_____ box.

_____ long skipping rope.

_____ skipping rope.

Join.

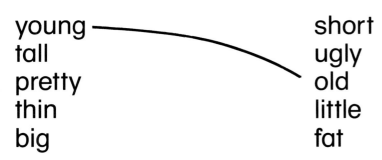

young	short
tall	ugly
pretty	old
thin	little
big	fat

Trace and write.

a	apple	f	k	
b	b	g	l	
c		h	m	
d		i	n	
e		j		

Trace and join.

K k   L l   M m   N n

mother   kite   notebook   lion

Circle and write.

K
L
M
N

___ ate

k
l
m
n

___ isten

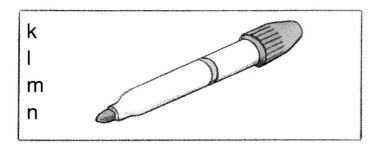

k
l
m
n

___ arker

k
l
m
n

___ ine

50

Join and trace.

play with a yo-yo

throw a ball

kick a ball

hit a ball

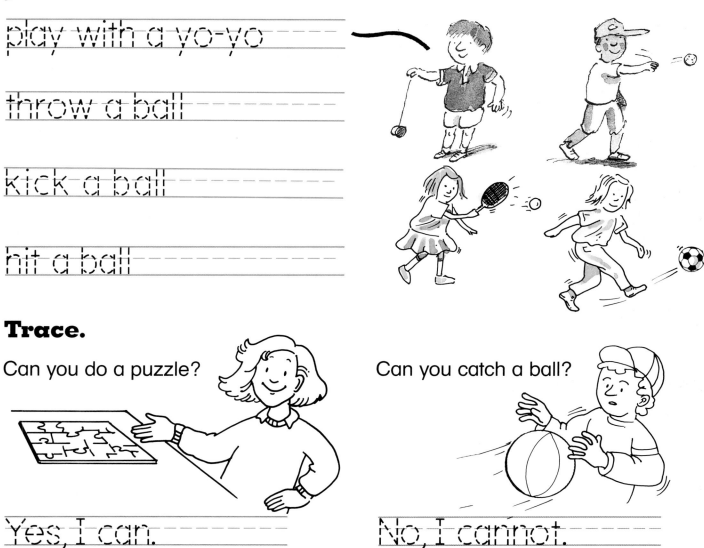

Trace.

Can you do a puzzle?

Yes, I can.

Can you catch a ball?

No, I cannot.

Write.

Can you hit a ball?

Join, trace, and write.

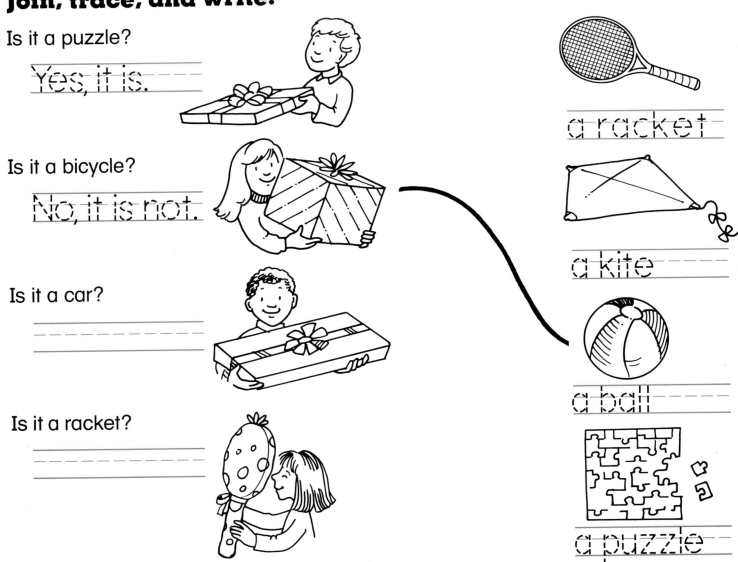

Is it a puzzle?

Yes, it is.

Is it a bicycle?

No, it is not.

Is it a car?

Is it a racket?

a racket

a kite

a ball

a puzzle

Circle and write.

What is it?

a big robot

a little robot

It is _____.

Unit 6

Trace.

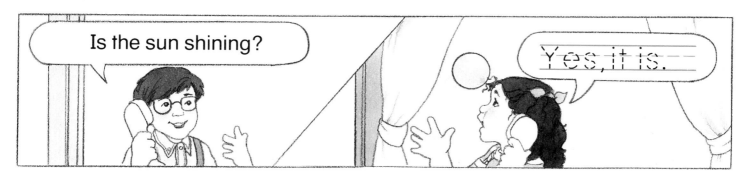

Join and trace.

The sun's shining.

The wind's blowing.

It's snowing.

It's raining.

Write and draw.

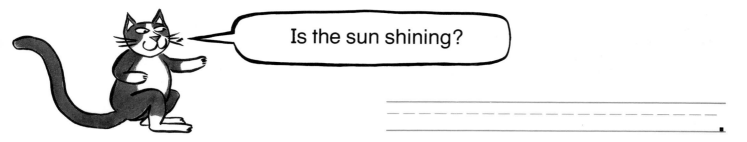

Is the sun shining?

Circle.

a flower

flowers

a cloud

clouds

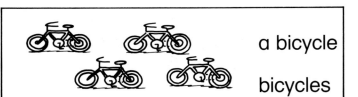
a bicycle

bicycles

a table

tables

Circle and write.

How many puddles are there?

six puddles

seven puddles

There are _____.

How many trees are there?

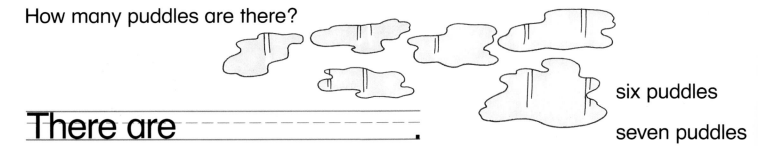

four trees

five trees

There are _____.

How many clouds are there?

one cloud

two clouds

There is _____.

Trace and write.

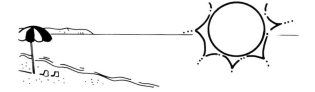

The sun's shining.

It's

Trace and write.

How many?

There's one tree.

There are

Circle and trace.

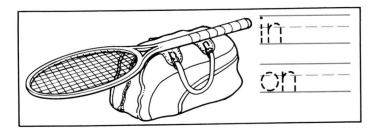

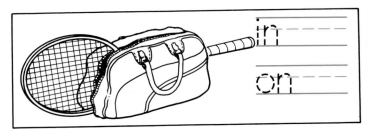

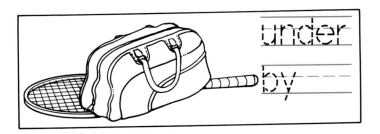

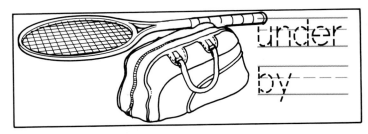

Circle and write.

Where is the book?

in

on

the bag

Where is the bicycle?

under

by

the tree

Where are the rackets?

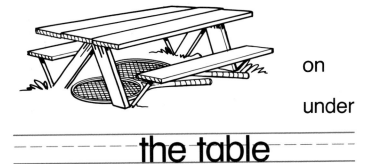

on

under

the table

Where are the balls?

by

in

the puddle

Trace and write.

Is it an octopus?

No, it isn't. It's a fish.

Is it a pencil?

Yes,

Is it a flower?

Is it a cloud?

Circle.   Yes/No

Is the cat on the table?   Yes   No
Is the cat by the dog?   Yes   No
Is the bag on the table?   Yes   No
Is the racket in the bag?   Yes   No
Is the book in the bag?   Yes   No
Is the pencil on the book?   Yes   No

Colour.

Colour the racket yellow.
Colour the dog brown.
Colour the bag blue and red.
Colour the cat black.
Colour the book green.
Colour the pencil orange.

Write.

O o   __ ctopus   __ pen   o

P p   __ en   __ encil   p

Q q   __ uiet   __ uestion   q

R r   __ uler   __ ed   r

Circle and trace.

o p q r

old

o p q r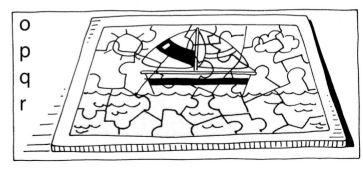

puzzle

o p q r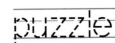

question

o p q r

robot

Trace and circle.

Is he playing tennis?

Yes, he is.

No, he isn't.

Is she climbing a tree?

Yes, she is.

No, she isn't.

Is he riding a bicycle?

Yes, he is.

No, he isn't.

Is she playing tag?

Yes, she is.

No, she isn't.

Is he reading a book?

Yes, he is.

No, he isn't.

Is she flying a kite?

Yes, she is.

No, she isn't.

Circle and say.

It is windy.

It is sunny.

It is raining.

It is snowing.

Trace and draw.

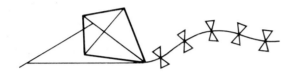

It is on the table.

It is under the table.

They are by the table.

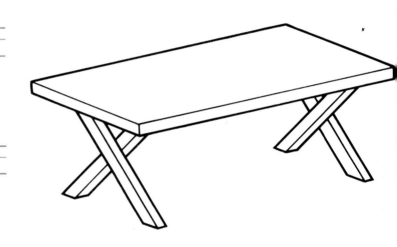

Trace and write.

How many kites are there?

How many trees are there?

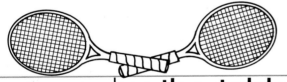

There are _____ kites.

There is _____ tree.

60

Review

1. Write and trace.

k l m n o p q r

_ite   _ion   _ouse

_uler   _otebook

_uestion   _encil   _ctopus

2. Find the words.

kite   bicycle   yo-yo

box

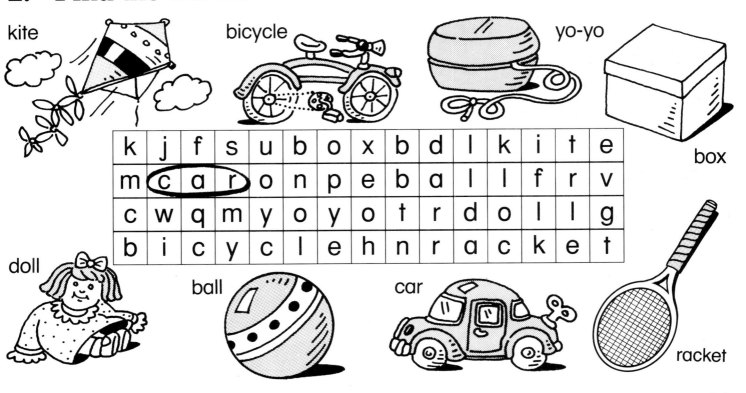

k	j	f	s	u	b	o	x	b	d	l	k	i	t	e
m	c	a	r	o	n	p	e	b	a	l	l	f	r	v
c	w	q	m	y	o	y	o	t	r	d	o	l	l	g
b	i	c	y	c	l	e	h	n	r	a	c	k	e	t

doll   ball   car   racket

61

3. **Join and trace.**

big

long

round

little

short

square

4. **Join and trace.**

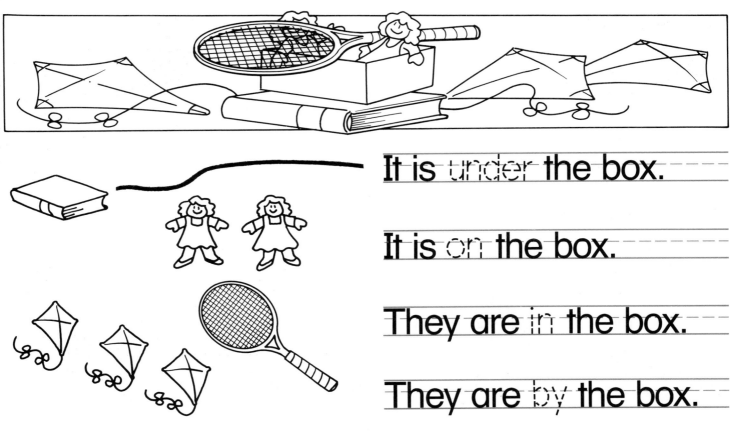

It is under the box.

It is on the box.

They are in the box.

They are by the box.

Unit 7

Trace.

an apple

some juice

Trace and say.

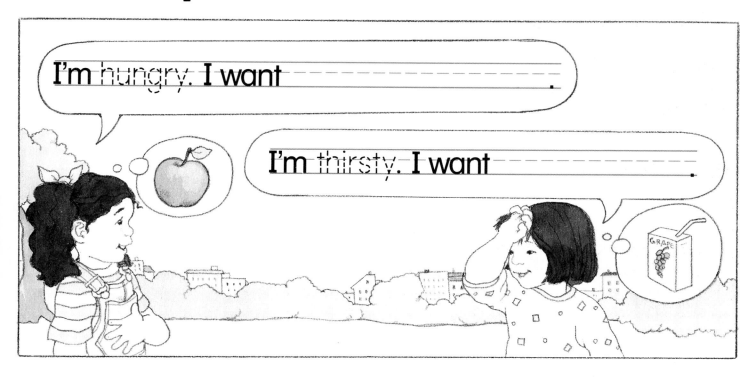

I'm hungry. I want _____.

I'm thirsty. I want _____.

Trace and say.

Here you are.

Thank you.

You're welcome.

Trace.

MENU

pizza

milk

bread

fish

ice cream

rice

chicken

cake

Write and draw.

What do you want?

I want ——————— and ——————— .

Trace and write.

I/climb/tree

He/fly/kite

She/ride/bicycle

I/play/tennis

He/read/book

I'm climbing a tree.

He's

Write.

John: I'm   . I want a peach.

Jenny: I'm   . I   some juice.

John: Here   .

Jenny: Thank   .

John: welcome.

I'm   .

I'm   .

Trace.

Do you want some ice cream?

No, I do not.

Do you want some pizza?

Yes, I do.

Circle and write.

Do you want some rice?

Yes, I do.

No, I do not.

Do you want some fish?

Yes, I do.

No, I do not.

Do you want some cake?

Yes, I do.

No, I do not.

Do you want some bread?

Yes, I do.

No, I do not.

Trace and write.

Do you want some chicken?
No, I don't. I want some fish.
Do you want some cake?
Yes, I do.

Trace and write.

No, I don't.

There's one cloud.

I'm hungry.

You're welcome.

Where's the kite?

I'm reading a book.

They're under the table.

No, I do not.

Join and trace.

S s
T t
U u
V v

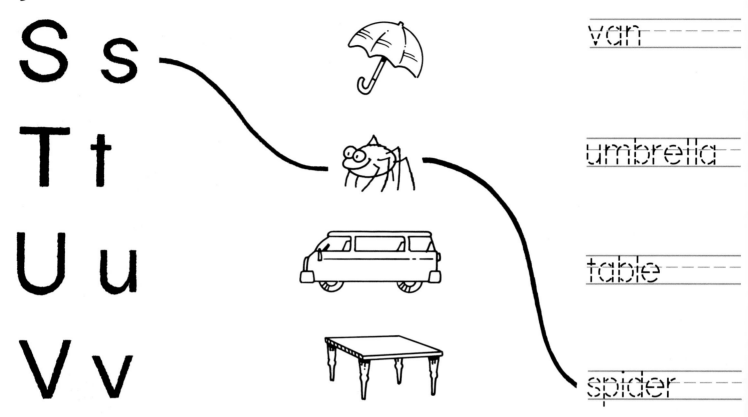

van

umbrella

table

spider

Circle and trace.

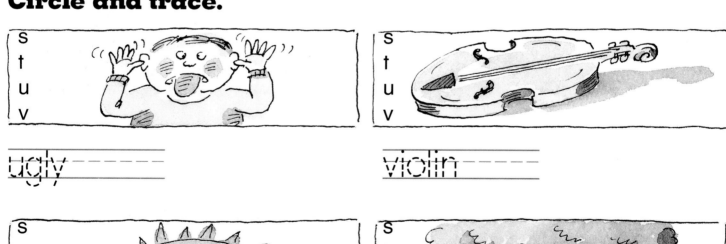

s
t
u
v

ugly

s
t
u
v

violin

s
t
u
v

sunny

s
t
u
v

tree

68

Trace and write.

I'm buying some milk.   I'm opening it.

I'm _____

Trace and join.

I'm buying an apple.
I'm washing it.
I'm cutting it.
I'm eating it.

Circle.   Yes/No

Can you eat it?   Can you drink it?

Yes   No

Yes   No

Yes   No

Yes   No

Write.

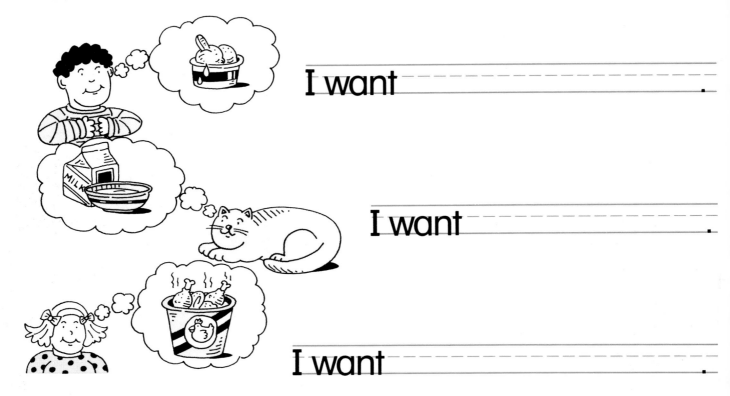

I want _____.

I want _____.

I want _____.

Circle and write.

Do you want some ice cream and some fish?

_____

Yes, I do.

No, I do not.

Do you want some ice cream and some cake?

Yes, I do.

No, I do not.

70

Unit 8

Trace, write, and colour.

Colour and write.

I like _____ .

Join and trace.

cats

dogs

rabbits

spiders

birds

frogs

Draw and write.

What do you like?

I like _____.

72

Join the questions and the answers.

What do you like?
What's your favourite colour?
What do you want?
What's he doing?
Where are the apples?
How many plums are there?
What are you doing?

Red.
I want some ice cream.
They're on the tree.
I like frogs.
He's climbing the tree.
I'm playing tag.
There's one.

Trace and write.

What do you like?

I like frogs.

Trace and write.

There's a plum. I like plums.

Trace.

Do you like spiders?

No, I do not.

Do you like cats?

Yes, I do.

Write.

Do you like rabbits?

Do you like frogs?

Do you like dogs?

Do you like birds?

Join and trace.

W w X x Y y Z z

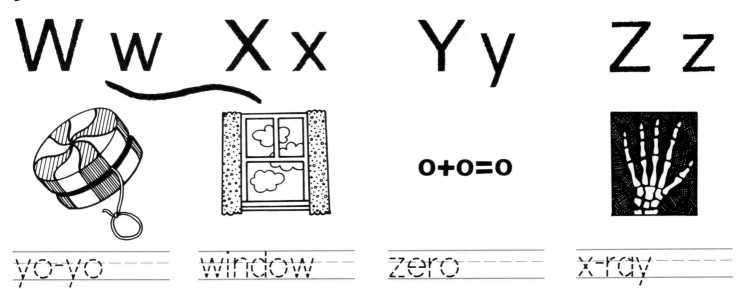

0+0=0

yo-yo   window   zero   x-ray

Trace and join.

Trace and join.

I'm swimming.

I'm hopping.

I'm walking.

I'm running.

I'm jumping.

I'm flying.

Trace.

| Can it fly? | Can it walk? |

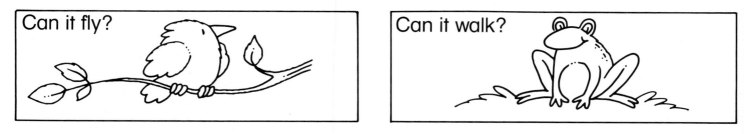

Yes, it can.   No, it cannot.

Write.

| Can it hop? | Can it swim? |

Trace and write.

I'm walking.

I'm

Trace and join.

I'm flying.

I'm hopping.

I'm swimming.

I'm drinking.

Circle.   Yes/No

Can it run?   Yes   No

Can it fly?   Yes   No

Can it hop?   Yes   No

Can it swim?   Yes   No

Write.

Look! There is ——————— .

Look! There is ——————— .

a bird

a dog

Circle, trace, and write.

What do you like?

dogs

cats

I like ——————— .

What do you like?

frogs

spiders

I like ——————— .

Circle and write.

Do you like cats?

Yes, I do.

No, I do not.

————————————

Do you like spiders?

Yes, I do.

No, I do not.

————————————

Review

1. Write.

Down

1.

2.

3.

4.

6. **0+0=0**

8.

9.

10.

12.

13.

16.

18.

Across

3.   5.   7.   9.

11.    14. 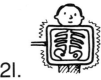   15.

17.    19.   20.   21.

2. Trace, write, and join.

dogs   cats   birds   frogs

dribs _____   tcsa _____

grofs _____   sodg   dogs _____

What do you like?

I like _____.

3. Join, write, and trace.

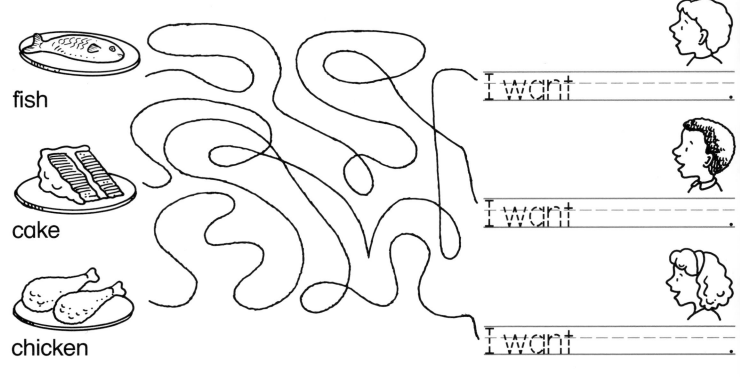

fish

cake

chicken

I want _____.

I want _____.

I want _____.

80